A SPECIAL GIFT FOR

FROM

A FATHER' *Legacy*

*Your Life Story
in Your Own Words*

BOK4303

Published in 2006 under license from J. Countryman, a trademark
of Thomas Nelson, Inc. exclusively for Hallmark Cards, Inc.

Visit us on the Web at www.Hallmark.com

© 2006 by J. Countryman, a division of Thomas Nelson Inc.
Nashville, TN 37214

Text © 2006 by J. Countryman and Hallmark Cards, Inc.

www.jcountryman.com

ISBN 1-59530-101-1

Designed by Koechel Peterson & Associates, Minneapolis, MN

Printed and bound in China

Contents

INTRODUCTION

As the years slip past we become more and more aware of what's really important in life. With every passing season we see more clearly and know more surely that the love and traditions a family shares are treasures beyond value.

Lying within our memories are the personal histories of those treasures—the dreams we've shared, the laughter and the tears, the triumphs and failures, the sad partings and joyous reunions—all the events big and small that are part of a family's constant love. These are among the things that mean the most.

Our memories are a gift that can be bestowed upon loved ones. By sharing them, we pass a loving legacy to children, grandchildren, and generations yet to come. Now and always our memories are a wellspring of the timeless bonds that keep us close at heart.

Personal
P O R T R A I T

Every good father

is a successful man.

WHAT IS YOUR DATE AND PLACE OF BIRTH?

WHAT IS YOUR FULL GIVEN NAME?

WHO SELECTED YOUR NAME?

WHY WERE YOU GIVEN THIS NAME?

DID YOU HAVE A NICKNAME?
How did you get it?

YOUR MOTHER'S FULL NAME
the date and place of her birth

YOUR FATHER'S FULL NAME
the date and place of his birth

THE NAMES OF YOUR SIBLINGS
the dates and places of their births

THE NAMES OF YOUR MATERNAL GRANDPARENTS
the dates and places of their births

THE NAMES OF YOUR PATERNAL GRANDPARENTS
the dates and places of their births

YOUR WIFE'S FULL GIVEN NAME
the date and place of her birth

WHAT ARE THE NAMES OF YOUR CHILDREN?
the dates and places of their births

WHAT ARE THE NAMES OF YOUR GRANDCHILDREN?
the dates and places of their births

WHAT IS YOUR FAVORITE WAY
TO SPEND A DAY OF LEISURE?

WHAT SPORT DO YOU LIKE THE MOST?
Why?

DO YOU HAVE A FAVORITE TEAM?

WHAT IS YOUR FAVORITE VACATION SPOT?
Why?

WHAT MEAL DO YOU MOST ENJOY?

DO YOU HAVE A FAVORITE SONG?
Is there some association that makes this song special to you?

WHAT ARE YOUR CURRENT AND PAST
FAVORITE TELEVISION SHOWS?

IS THERE A MOVIE YOU HAVE WATCHED REPEATEDLY
BECAUSE YOU LIKE IT SO MUCH?
What makes it so enjoyable?

WHAT HOBBIES OR ACTIVITIES DO YOU ENJOY MOST?

WHAT KINDS OF SOCIAL GATHERINGS
DO YOU ENJOY MOST?

WHAT IS YOUR GREATEST ABILITY OR TALENT?
How have you used it throughout your life?

WHAT IS YOUR BEST CHARACTERISTIC?

IS THERE A CHARACTERISTIC YOU WISH YOU COULD CHANGE ABOUT YOURSELF?

DESCRIBE A TYPICAL DAY
IN YOUR LIFE RIGHT NOW.

Childhood

The world is filled with wonder
when you see it through
the eyes of a child.

DESCRIBE YOUR CHILDHOOD NEIGHBORHOOD

DESCRIBE YOUR CHILDHOOD HOME

WHAT WAS YOUR FAVORITE ROOM IN THIS HOME?
What made it special?

WHAT CHORES DID YOU HAVE TO DO?

DID YOU GET AN ALLOWANCE?
How much was it?

WHAT INDOOR ACTIVITY DID YOU MOST ENJOY?
Why?

WHAT WAS YOUR FAVORITE SPORT
OR OUTDOOR ACTIVITY?

DID YOU HAVE ANY SPECIAL TALENTS AS A CHILD?

DO YOU REMEMBER ANY FAVORITE TOYS?

DID YOU EVER HAVE A HIDEAWAY, CLUBHOUSE,
OR OTHER SPECIAL PLACE THAT WAS "YOURS"?
Describe this place.

WHAT WAS AN ESPECIALLY FUN OUTING
FOR YOU AS A CHILD?

WHICH FRIENDS FROM YOUR CHILDHOOD DO YOU MOST REMEMBER?

DID YOU ENJOY READING AS A BOY?
If so, what did you like to read?

DID YOU ATTEND CHURCH OR SERVICE
OF ANY KIND AS A YOUNG BOY?
What are your earliest memories of this experience?

WERE YOU BAPTIZED OR DEDICATED AS AN INFANT?
Where? By whom?

WHAT CHILDHOOD EXPERIENCES
DO YOU FEEL SHAPED YOU THE MOST?

WHAT FROM YOUR CHILDHOOD
ARE YOU MOST THANKFUL FOR?

Family LIFE

A family is a circle of love…
formed by memories,
filled with devotion.

WHAT IS A FAVORITE MEMORY
OF YOUR FATHER FROM YOUR CHILDHOOD?
Why this memory?

WHAT WAS YOUR FATHER'S ATTITUDE TOWARD LIFE?
How did his attitude affect you?

WHAT DID YOU ENJOY DOING WITH YOUR FATHER?

IN WHAT WAYS ARE YOU LIKE YOUR FATHER?

HOW WOULD YOU FINISH THIS SENTENCE?
"One thing my dad always said was…"

WHAT WORK DID YOUR FATHER DO?
Did it interest you?

WHAT IS A FAVORITE MEMORY
OF YOUR MOTHER FROM YOUR CHILDHOOD?
Why this memory?

WHAT WAS YOUR MOTHER'S ATTITUDE TOWARD LIFE?
How did her attitude affect you?

IN WHAT WAYS ARE YOU LIKE YOUR MOTHER?

WHAT DID YOU ENJOY DOING WITH YOUR MOM?

WHAT WORK DID YOUR MOTHER DO?
Did it interest you?

WHAT WERE YOUR FAMILY CIRCUMSTANCES
WHEN YOU WERE GROWING UP?
How did they affect you?

WHAT RESPONSIBILITIES DID YOUR PARENTS
REQUIRE OF YOU AS YOU WERE GROWING UP?

HAS THAT INFLUENCED YOU
IN THE WAY YOU'VE RAISE YOUR CHILDREN?

WHAT TALENTS, ABILITIES OR QUALITIES
DID YOUR PARENTS NURTURE IN YOU?

WHAT KIND OF PERSON
DID YOUR PARENTS ENCOURAGE YOU TO BE?

IF YOU HAVE SIBLINGS, LIST ANY
SPECIAL MEMORIES THAT YOU HAVE
OF EACH OF THEM.

WHAT MISCHIEVOUS THINGS DID YOU DO
WITH YOUR SIBLINGS...OR TO THEM?

HOW DID YOU AND YOUR SIBLINGS GET ALONG?

WHEN YOU WERE GROWING UP,
DID YOU HAVE ANY PETS?

WHAT DID YOU MOST ENJOY
ABOUT HAVING A PET?

WHAT DID YOUR FAMILY
MOST ENJOY DOING TOGETHER?

WHAT ARE YOUR EARLY
MEMORIES OF YOUR GRANDPARENTS?

WHERE DID THEY LIVE?

WHAT KIND OF WORK DID THEY DO?

WHAT DO YOU REMEMBER
ABOUT GOING TO VISIT THEM
OR ABOUT THEM VISITING YOU?

WHAT DID YOU ENJOY
MOST ABOUT YOUR GRANDPARENTS?

WHAT IS ONE VALUABLE LESSON
YOU LEARNED FROM THEM?

WHAT MEMORIES OR KNOWLEDGE DO YOU HAVE ABOUT YOUR GREAT-GRANDPARENTS?

WHAT DO YOU KNOW ABOUT YOUR ANCESTORS' ETHNIC OR NATIONAL ORIGINS?

WHAT WAS YOUR FAVORITE
HOME-COOKED MEAL?

WHAT SNACKS AND SPECIAL TREATS
DID YOUR FAMILY ENJOY?

WHEN THE FAMILY WENT OUT TO DINNER,
WHAT WERE YOUR FAVORITE PLACES TO GO AND
YOUR FAVORITE THINGS TO ORDER?

DID YOUR FAMILY OFTEN HAVE COMPANY?

WHAT WERE YOUR FAMILY SUMMER OUTINGS LIKE?
Where did you go and what did you do?

WHAT DID YOUR FAMILY DO
FOR FUN IN THE WINTER?

DID YOUR FAMILY ATTEND FAMILY REUNIONS?
What did you most enjoy about the reunions?

DID YOU HAVE CLOSE RELATIONSHIPS WITH
ANY OF YOUR AUNTS, UNCLES, OR COUSINS?
Why were these relationships important to you?

WHAT ARE THE FIRST FEW WORDS THAT
COME TO MIND WHEN YOU THINK OF YOUR FAMILY?
Why these words?

Education

Knowledge is the power

that gives us wings to soar.

WHERE DID YOU ATTEND ELEMENTARY SCHOOL?
How did you travel between school and home?

WHAT ARE YOUR EARLIEST MEMORIES
OF ATTENDING SCHOOL?

WHAT DID YOU ENJOY
MOST ABOUT ELEMENTARY SCHOOL?

WHAT DID YOU LIKE LEAST?

WHERE DID YOU ATTEND MIDDLE SCHOOL?
How did you travel there each day?

WHERE DID YOU ATTEND HIGH SCHOOL
AND HOW DID YOU TRAVEL THERE EACH DAY?

WHAT WERE YOUR FAVORITE SUBJECTS IN MIDDLE SCHOOL AND HIGH SCHOOL?
Why?

WHAT EXTRACURRICULAR ACTIVITIES DID YOU ENJOY MOST?
Why did you choose these activities?

DID YOU RECEIVE ANY SPECIAL AWARDS OR RECOGNITION THROUGHOUT YOUR EDUCATION?

WHO WAS YOUR FAVORITE TEACHER?
How did that teacher influence you?

WHAT WERE THE FASHION TRENDS FROM YOUR SCHOOL DAYS?
Did you participate in them? Why or why not?

WHAT POPULAR SONGS DO YOU REMEMBER?

MOVIES?

TELEVISION SHOWS?

WHO WERE THE POPULAR CELEBRITIES?

WHAT KIND OF DANCES
AND PARTIES DID YOU ATTEND?

IF YOU HAD A CAR DURING
YOUR HIGH SCHOOL YEARS, WHAT KIND WAS IT?
Were you proud of it?

WHAT WAS DIFFICULT ABOUT YOUR
MIDDLE SCHOOL AND HIGH SCHOOL YEARS?

WHAT ARE YOU ESPECIALLY GLAD YOU DID
DURING YOUR MIDDLE SCHOOL
AND HIGH SCHOOL YEARS?

WHAT WERE YOUR GOALS AND ASPIRATIONS FOR LIFE AS YOU GRADUATED FROM HIGH SCHOOL?
How did these change with time?

WHAT PATH DID YOU CHOOSE
AFTER GRADUATING FROM HIGH SCHOOL?

IF YOU ATTENDED A COLLEGE OR
A CAREER TRAINING SCHOOL, WHAT DID YOU
CHOOSE AS YOUR FIELD OF STUDY?

IF YOU MOVED AWAY FROM HOME
IN ORDER TO PURSUE YOUR EDUCATION,
DESCRIBE THIS EXPERIENCE.

WHAT WAS YOUR FIRST
APARTMENT OR DORM ROOM LIKE?

WHAT ARE SOME OF YOUR FAVORITE
COLLEGE MEMORIES?

On the Job

Any job can be made great.
It's the worker—not the work—
that counts.

HOW DID YOU EARN MONEY
WHEN YOU WERE YOUNG?

WHO GAVE YOU YOUR FIRST REGULAR PAYING JOB?
What kind of job was it? What did it pay?

WHAT WAS YOUR FIRST CAREER-ORIENTED JOB?
What did you do at this job?

WHAT WERE YOUR FEELINGS
WHEN YOU RECEIVED THIS FIRST JOB?

WHAT DID YOU LIKE ABOUT THIS JOB?

WHAT WAS THE MOST ENJOYABLE JOB
YOU EVER HAD?
What made it enjoyable?

WHAT WAS THE WORST JOB YOU EVER HAD?
Why did you dislike it?

WHAT HAS BEEN YOUR MOST REWARDING JOB?
In what ways was it rewarding?

HAVE ANY OF YOUR JOBS FORCED YOU TO MOVE?
Were you happy about moving?

HAVE ANY OF YOUR JOBS INVOLVED BUSINESS TRAVEL?
What was the most memorable place you visited for your work?

WAS A CO-WORKER OR SUPERIOR
EVER A VALUABLE MENTOR TO YOU?
What did you learn from that person?

DID YOU EVER MENTOR SOMEONE?
Was doing so a good experience for you?

WHAT SPECIAL FRIENDS
DID YOU MAKE AS A RESULT OF YOUR WORK?

WHAT KIND OF WORK
DO YOU ENJOY DOING AROUND THE HOUSE?

WHAT KIND WOULD YOU PREFER TO AVOID?

Love
AND
Marriage

When love touches our hearts,

happiness fills our days.

WHO WAS YOUR FIRST CRUSH?

WHEN DID YOU ATTEND
YOUR FIRST BOY/GIRL PARTY?

WHAT DO YOU REMEMBER
ABOUT YOUR FIRST KISS?

WHAT DO YOU REMEMBER
ABOUT YOUR FIRST DATE?

WHAT WAS A TYPICAL DATE LIKE AT THAT TIME?

WHO WAS YOUR FIRST LOVE?
What did you learn from this relationship?

HOW OLD WERE YOU WHEN YOU MET YOUR WIFE?

HOW DID YOU MEET HER?

WHAT QUALITIES ATTRACTED YOU TO HER?

WHAT WAS YOUR FIRST IMPRESSION OF HER?
How did this impression change with time?

HOW LONG WAS YOUR COURTSHIP?

WHAT DID YOU ENJOY DOING TOGETHER?

WHEN DID YOU KNOW
THAT SHE WAS "THE ONE"?
How did you know?

WHAT WAS THE MARRIAGE PROPOSAL LIKE?

WHAT WAS THE DATE
AND PLACE OF THE WEDDING?

WHAT DID YOU WEAR?

WHAT DID SHE WEAR?

HOW MANY GUESTS ATTENDED THE WEDDING?

DID YOU HAVE A SPECIAL "FIRST DANCE" SONG?
Why did you choose this song?

WHAT IS YOUR MOST OUTSTANDING MEMORY
FROM YOUR WEDDING DAY?

WHERE DID YOU GO ON YOUR HONEYMOON?
Recall a special moment or event from the honeymoon.

WHERE DID YOU LIVE
RIGHT AFTER YOU GOT MARRIED?
What do you remember about it most vividly?

DESCRIBE A TYPICAL DINNER
AND EVENING DURING YOUR EARLY MARRIAGE.

WHEN DID YOU START
THINKING ABOUT HAVING CHILDREN?
What about having children did you look forward to most?

WHO WERE SOME OF YOUR CLOSEST FRIENDS WHEN YOU WERE FIRST MARRIED?

What were some of the fun things you did with them?

WHAT LEISURE ACTIVITIES OR ENTERTAINMENTS DID YOU AND YOUR WIFE ENJOY?

WHAT HAVE YOU FOUND
MOST REWARDING ABOUT MARRIAGE?

WHAT DO YOU THINK IS MOST IMPORTANT
IN MAINTAINING A HEALTHY MARRIAGE?

HAS THERE BEEN AN EVENT IN YOUR MARRIAGE WHEN SHARING AND PARTNERSHIP WERE PARTICULARLY IMPORTANT?

WHAT DO YOU VALUE ABOUT
THE DAY-TO-DAY RELATIONSHIP THAT YOU
AND YOUR WIFE SHARE NOW?

Parenting

To be a father is to protect,

nurture, and guide,

but most of all, to love.

HOW DID YOU FEEL
WHEN YOU FIRST LEARNED THAT YOU
WERE TO BECOME A FATHER?

WHERE DID YOU LIVE
WHEN YOUR FIRST CHILD WAS BORN?

DESCRIBE YOUR CIRCUMSTANCES AT THAT TIME.

WHAT WERE YOUR STRONGEST FEELINGS
WHEN YOU FIRST HAD A NEWBORN AT HOME?

HOW DID BECOMING A FATHER
CHANGE YOUR OUTLOOK ON LIFE?

WHAT IS YOUR MOST VIVID MEMORY
OF YOUR CHILDREN'S EARLY YEARS?

WHAT ACTIVITIES DID YOU MOST ENJOY
WITH YOUR CHILDREN WHEN THEY WERE YOUNG?

WHAT DID YOU AND YOUR WIFE DO
FOR CHILD-FREE ENTERTAINMENT AT THAT TIME?

WHAT SIMILARITIES DO YOU SEE
BETWEEN YOURSELF AND YOUR CHILDREN?

WHAT SIMILARITIES DO YOU SEE
AMONG YOUR CHILDREN?

WHAT VALUES DID YOU TRY
TO NURTURE IN YOUR CHILDREN?

WHAT HAS BEEN YOUR GREATEST JOY
IN BEING A FATHER?

WHAT HAS BEEN THE GREATEST CHALLENGE?

HOW HAS YOUR CHILDREN'S UPBRINGING
BEEN DIFFERENT FROM OR SIMILAR TO YOUR OWN?

IS THERE ANYTHING YOU KNOW NOW
THAT YOU WISH YOU'D KNOWN WHEN YOU
FIRST BECAME A FATHER?

WHAT ARE THE THINGS YOU HOPE
YOUR CHILDREN HAVE LEARNED FROM YOU?

WHAT IS THE MOST IMPORTANT THING
YOU'VE LEARNED FROM BEING A FATHER?

Celebrations

Life offers so many

wonderful things to share,

so many special joys to celebrate.

HOW WAS YOUR BIRTHDAY CELEBRATED
WHEN YOU WERE YOUNG?

WHAT IS YOUR FONDEST MEMORY
OF A BIRTHDAY CELEBRATION?

DO YOU REMEMBER PARTICULARLY SPECIAL
BIRTHDAY GIFTS YOU RECEIVED?
What made them so special?

DID YOU REQUEST ANY SPECIAL MEALS
OR DESSERTS ON YOUR BIRTHDAYS?

DID YOU EVER HAVE A THEME PARTY
OR OTHERWISE UNIQUE CELEBRATION?
If yes, describe it.

HOW DID YOU CELEBRATE CHRISTMAS AS A CHILD?

WHAT CHILDHOOD CHRISTMAS
STANDS OUT THE MOST IN YOUR MEMORY?

WHAT WAS YOUR FAVORITE
CHRISTMAS FOOD DURING YOUR CHILDHOOD?

WHAT WAS YOUR FAVORITE CHRISTMAS CAROL?
Is it still your favorite?

DID YOU HAVE A SPECIAL CHRISTMAS STOCKING
OR ORNAMENT WHEN YOU WERE A CHILD?
Do you know where it came from?

DESCRIBE AN ESPECIALLY MEMORABLE CHRISTMAS GIFT YOU RECEIVED.

Who was it from?

DESCRIBE AN ESPECIALLY MEMORABLE CHRISTMAS GIFT YOU GAVE.

Who was it for?

WHAT CHRISTMAS TRADITIONS
FROM YOUR CHILDHOOD DID YOU PASS ON
TO YOUR CHILDREN?

WHAT HAS BEEN THE MOST MEANINGFUL
CHRISTMAS FOR YOU AS A PARENT?

HOW DID YOU CELEBRATE THANKSGIVING?
Did you have a favorite Thanksgiving tradition?

HOW DID YOU CELEBRATE A TYPICAL
FOURTH OF JULY WHEN YOU WERE A CHILD?

DID YOU ENJOY DRESSING UP
FOR HALLOWEEN TO TRICK-OR-TREAT?
Do you remember an especially fun costume?
What was your favorite Halloween treat?

WHAT IS A PARTICULARLY MEANINGFUL
MEMORY FROM A HOLIDAY CELEBRATION?

Life
EVENTS

Moment by moment,
day by day,
families create a lifetime of memories.

WHAT WAS THE HAPPIEST TIME OF YOUR LIFE?

WHAT WAS THE SADDEST?

WHAT WAS THE BUSIEST TIME OF YOUR LIFE?

WHAT WAS THE MOST RELAXED?

WHAT EVENT WOULD YOU SAY
HAS PARTICULARLY IMPACTED YOUR LIFE?

HAS THERE BEEN A POLITICAL EVENT
IN YOUR LIFETIME THAT MADE A STRONG
IMPRESSION ON YOU?

HAVE YOU OR OTHER FAMILY MEMBERS SERVED IN THE MILITARY?
What are your feelings about this?

WHAT HAVE YOU DONE IN YOUR LIFE
THAT YOU ARE ESPECIALLY PROUD OF?

HAVE YOU EVER BEEN IN AN ACCIDENT, HAD MAJOR SURGERY, OR A LONG ILLNESS?
If so, did it have a lasting effect on you?

DID TRAGEDY EVER OCCUR IN YOUR FAMILY OR WITH A LOVED ONE?
How did you respond to it?

WHAT WAS THE MOST DIFFICULT CHOICE
YOU HAD TO MAKE IN YOUR LIFE?
Would you make the same choice again?

DESCRIBE YOUR MOST MEMORABLE
TRAVEL EXPERIENCE.

WHEN DID YOU TAKE YOUR FIRST AIRPLANE TRIP?
Where did you go?

DID YOU EVER TRAVEL ABROAD?
What was your reaction?

WHAT IS THE MOST FUN, INTERESTING,
OR EXCITING PLACE YOU'VE EVER VISITED?
What made it so?

HAVE YOU EVER HELPED SOMEONE IN NEED?
If so, how?

HAVE YOU EVER DEDICATED YOURSELF
TO A CAUSE OR ORGANIZATION?
Why was it important to you?

DID YOU EVER PLAY ON A SPORTS TEAM
OR PARTICIPATE IN ANOTHER COMPETITIVE ACTIVITY?
How did you benefit from it?

HAVE YOU EVER RECEIVED
PROFESSIONAL RECOGNITION?
If so, for what?
How did it make you feel?

WHAT DO YOU REGARD AS THE MOST IMPORTANT INVENTION IN YOUR LIFETIME?
How did it affect you?

WHAT DO YOU SEE AS THE MOST
IMPORTANT POLITICAL OR INTERNATIONAL
EVENTS OF YOUR LIFETIME?

WHAT SCIENTIFIC DISCOVERIES
OR ADVANCES HAVE INTERESTED YOU THE MOST?

IN WHAT WAYS DO YOU THINK SOCIETY
HAS CHANGED THE MOST SINCE YOUR YOUTH?

WHAT IS ONE THING YOU WOULD NEVER CHANGE
ABOUT THE WAY YOU'VE LIVED YOUR LIFE?

WHAT IS ONE THING YOU WISH
YOU HAD DONE DIFFERENTLY IN YOUR LIFE?
Why?

WHAT ARE YOUR HOPES FOR YOURSELF
AND YOUR FAMILY IN THE NEXT TEN YEARS?

WHAT ARE YOUR HOPES
FOR NATIONAL OR WORLD EVENTS?

Inspiration

How great it is

to have the freedom to dream

and the opportunity

to make those dreams come true.

WHAT PEOPLE HAVE MADE THE GREATEST
IMPACT ON YOUR LIFE?

How?

WHO HAVE YOU TURNED TO
MOST OFTEN FOR ADVICE OR GUIDANCE?

DOES RELIGION PLAY
A SIGNIFICANT ROLE IN YOUR LIFE?

IS THERE A POEM, PASSAGE, OR QUOTE
THAT HAS BEEN MEANINGFUL IN YOUR LIFE?
Why is it important to you?

IF YOU COULD KEEP ONLY ONE FAMILY PHOTO,
WHICH WOULD IT BE?
Why?

WHAT IS YOUR MOST TREASURED POSSESSION?
Why is it of value?

WHAT DO YOU CONSIDER
TO BE YOUR LIFE'S GREATEST GIFTS?

HAVE YOU EVER FELT
THAT YOU HAD A SPECIAL CALLING?

WHO WERE YOUR ROLE MODELS
WHEN YOU WERE YOUNG?

DID YOU PARTICULARLY ADMIRE A FAMOUS PERSON?
What made this person admirable?

HAVE YOU EVER LISTENED TO A PUBLIC SPEAKER
WHO MADE A BIG IMPRESSION ON YOU?
If not, who would you like to hear and why?

IS THERE AN AUTHOR OR BOOK
THAT HAS INFLUENCED YOU IN A UNIQUE WAY?
What are some of the insights that you've received?

WHAT VALUABLE ADVICE DID YOU
RECEIVE FROM AN ADULT WHEN YOU WERE YOUNG?

What were the circumstances?

WHAT INSIGHTS CAN YOU SHARE
ABOUT WORKING WELL WITH OTHERS?

HOW WOULD YOU DESCRIBE SUCCESS?

WHAT DO YOU FEEL IS "THE SECRET TO SUCCESS"?

WHAT DO YOU THINK ARE THE
IMPORTANT CHARACTERISTICS OF A GOOD FRIEND?

WHAT DO YOU VALUE MOST ABOUT YOUR FAMILY?

WHAT IS THE MOST IMPORTANT LESSON
YOU HAVE LEARNED ABOUT LIFE?

WHAT ADVICE ABOUT LIFE
WOULD YOU LIKE YOUR FAMILY TO REMEMBER?

PLEASE RECORD ANY OTHER FAVORITE MEMORIES.

If you have enjoyed this book,
Hallmark would love
to hear from you.

Please send comments to

Book Feedback
2501 McGee, Mail Drop 215
Kansas City, MO 64141-6580

Or e-mail us at

booknotes@hallmark.com